# PHONICS
## for Reading

**FIRST LEVEL**

**Cover Design:** Pat Lucas
**Illustrator:** Leslie Alfred McGrath

**Anita Archer**
**James Flood**
**Diane Lapp**
**Linda Lungren**

CURRICULUM ASSOCIATES®, INC.

ISBN 978-0-89187-991-6

©2009, 2002, 1989—Curriculum Associates, Inc.
North Billerica, MA 01862

15  14  13  12  11  10  9  8  7  6  5  4  3  2

# Table of Contents

| Lesson | Page | Lesson | Page |
|---|---|---|---|
| Lesson 1 | 4 | Lesson 17 | 68 |
| Lesson 2 | 8 | Lesson 18 | 72 |
| Lesson 3 | 12 | Lesson 19 | 76 |
| Lesson 4 | 16 | Lesson 20 | 80 |
| Lesson 5 | 20 | Lesson 21 | 84 |
| Lesson 6 | 24 | Lesson 22 | 88 |
| Lesson 7 | 28 | Lesson 23 | 92 |
| Lesson 8 | 32 | Lesson 24 | 96 |
| Lesson 9 | 36 | Lesson 25 | 100 |
| Lesson 10 | 40 | Lesson 26 | 104 |
| Lesson 11 | 44 | Lesson 27 | 108 |
| Lesson 12 | 48 | Lesson 28 | 112 |
| Lesson 13 | 52 | Lesson 29 | 116 |
| Lesson 14 | 56 | Lesson 30 | 120 |
| Lesson 15 | 60 | Word Lists | 124 |
| Lesson 16 | 64 | | |

# LESSON 1

■ **New Sounds.** Say the words.

r<u>a</u>n          s<u>i</u>t

**A. New Words.** Say each sound. Say each word.

1.  <u>a</u> m          <u>i</u> n          S <u>a</u> m

2.  <u>a</u> n          N <u>a</u> n          f <u>i</u> t

3.  m <u>a</u> n        s <u>a</u> t        s <u>i</u> t

4.  f a t             s a d              l i p

5.  r i p             r a n              l a p

Circle the word that goes with each picture.

1.       am          in          (Sam)

2.       an          (Nan)       fit

3.       (man)       sat         sit

4.       fat         sad         (lip)

5.       (rip)       ran         lap

4

■ **Sight Words.** Say the words.

people    school    to    little    on    was    he    see    a    the

■ **Challenge Words.** Say the words.

admit    fabric    rabbit    rapid    attic
1  2      1  2      1  2      1  2      1  2

**B.    Sentences and Stories.** Read each story. Write the story number under the picture that goes with each story.

Story 1
    Sam ran <u>to school</u>.
    <u>He</u> had <u>a</u> hat.
    <u>The</u> hat <u>was little</u>.

_2_

**Story 2**
Nan had <u>a rabbit</u>.
<u>The rabbit</u> sat <u>on a</u> lap.
<u>The rabbit ran</u>.

_1_

**Story 3**
<u>The</u> man sat in <u>the attic</u>.
<u>The fabric</u> had <u>a</u> rip.
<u>He was</u> sad.

_3_

5

**C. Spelling.** Write the words and sentence that your teacher says.

1. _____    3. _____

2. _____    4. _____

5. _____

_____

**D. Practice Activity 1.** Change the first letter in each word to make another word that has the same ending. Write the letter on the line.

1. <u>f</u>  a  t  ➡   _S_  a  t

2. <u>r</u>  i  p  ➡   _L_  i  p

3. <u>m</u>  a  d  ➡   _S_  a  d

4. <u>N</u>  a  n  ➡   _R_  a  n

5. <u>s</u>  a  t  ➡   _S_  a  t

Correct

**E. Practice Activity 2.** Draw a line under the sentence that goes with each picture.

1. Sam ran to school.

<u>Sam sat in school.</u>

2. <u>He sat on a lap.</u>

He sat on a lip.

3. Nan had an attic.

<u>Nan had a rabbit.</u>

4. <u>My little rabbit ran.</u>

My little rabbit sat.

5. <u>The fabric has a lip.</u>

<u>The fabric has a rip.</u>

6. <u>He is fat.</u>

He is fit.

7. Sam and Nan sit.

<u>The man ran.</u>

8. <u>Nan is a little sad.</u>

Nan is in the attic.

# LESSON 2

**A. New Words.** Say each sound. Say each word.

1.  f <u>i</u> x      <u>a</u> d      w <u>a</u> x

2.  w <u>i</u> n      v <u>a</u> n      s <u>a</u> p

3.  s <u>i</u> p      m <u>a</u> d      l <u>i</u> d

4.  m a p      f i n      f a n

5.  r a t      s i x      m i x

Circle the word that goes with each picture.

1.   (fix)    ad    wax

2.   win    (van)    sap

3.   (sip)    mad    lid

4.   map    fin    (fan)

5.   rat    (six)    mix

■ **Sight Words.** Say the words.

water   you   are   my   was   people   school   little   to   on

---

■ **Challenge Words.** Say the words.

tidbit   limit   satin   valid   axis
 1  2      1  2     1  2     1  2     1  2

---

**B.   Sentences and Stories.** Read each story. Write the story number under the picture that goes with each story.

**Story 1**
Nan has a van
Six people can sit in the van.
The van is at school.

3

**Story 2**
The man has a fan.
The fan is satin.
The satin fan has a rip.

1

**Story 3**
The man has six maps.
The man can see water on the maps.
He can see ads on the maps.

2

**C. Spelling.** Write the words and sentence that your teacher says.

1. _fin_                          3. _rat_

2. _Lid_                          4. _six_

5. _nan has a van_

---

**D. Practice Activity 1.** Change the first letter in each word to make another word that has the same ending. Write the letter on the line.

1. <u>s</u> a p  ➡️  _m_ a p

2. <u>v</u> a n  ➡️  _f_ a n

3. <u>m</u> i x  ➡️  _s_ i x

4. <u>w</u> i n  ➡️  _f_ i n

5. <u>f</u> a t  ➡️  _r_ a t

Correct

**E. Practice Activity 2.** Draw a line under the sentence that goes
with each picture.

1. The man has my (map.)          The man has an ad.

2. Sam can win a map.          Sam can win a (van.)

3. <u>A cat ran to a (rat.)</u>          A rat ran to school.

4. Nan has six satin fins.          <u>Nan has six satin (fans.)</u>

5. <u>The can has a (lid.)</u>          The can has a rip.

6. Nan can mix.          <u>Nan can (sip.)</u>

7. Sam is in the van.          <u>Sam is in the (water.)</u>

8. <u>The people can wax the (van.)</u>          The people are in the van.

[ ] Correct

# LESSON 3

**A. New Words.** Say each sound. Say each word.

1. b <u>a</u> t          c <u>a</u> t          h <u>i</u> s

2. h <u>i</u> m          c <u>a</u> n          b <u>i</u> t

3. h <u>a</u> d          h <u>i</u> d          p <u>a</u> t

4. p i t          h i t          t a n

5. t i n          t a p          t i p

Circle the word that goes with each picture.

1.  (bat)          cat          his

2.  him          (can)          bit

3.  had          hid          (pat)

4.  (pit)          hit          tan

5.  tin          tap          (tip)

- ■ **Sight Words.** Say the words.

  have  her  and  we  he  little  water  people  see  to

- ■ **Challenge Words.** Say the words.

  cabin  catnip  hatpin  atlas  panic
  1 2    1 2     1 2     1 2    1 2

**B.  Sentences and Stories.** Read each story. Write the story number under the picture that goes with each story.

**Story 1**
Sam had a little catnip.
He hid it in the bag.
Can the cat have the catnip?

1

**Story 2**
Nan had a cat.
The cat sat on her lap.
Nan can pat the cat.

2

**Story 3**
We have a tin can in the cabin.
We can tap on the can.
We hid the can in the water.

3

**C. Spelling.** Write the words and sentence that your teacher says.

1. _Pat_

2. _can_

3. _him_

4. _had_

5. _Nan is sad_

**D. Practice Activity 1.** Fill in each blank with the best word.

1. Sam has a fat _cat_ .          hit    sat    cat

2. His cat _ran_ .          can    tan    ran

3. Sam can _pat_ the tan cat.          pat    pit    wax

4. The cat sees _him_ .          bat    his    him

5. The cat ran and _hid_ .          mix    hid    lid

6. Nan has a _tan_ bat.          tan    tap    fix

7. The _tip_ is tan.          tip    bit    sad

8. She hid the fan in the _tap_ can.          had    tap    can

9. Nan hit the _rip_ tin can.          rip    tip    tin

10. The can is in the _pit_ .          pat    pit    sip

Correct

E.  **Practice Activity 2.** Draw a line under the sentence that goes with each picture.

1.  Sam can pat the cat.

Sam hid the hatpin.

2.  He has a tan cat.

He has a tan tin.

3.  The tin can is in the water.

Sam had catnip.

4.  The rabbit is in the cabin.

His rabbit bit the tip.

5.  Nan can mix in the can.

Nan can tap on the lid.

6.  Sam and Nan mix wax.

Sam and Nan wax the van.

7.  Six people fit in the pit.

Sam and Nan fit in the van.

8.  The sad cat ran to Nan.

The sad cat ran to him.

Correct

15

# LESSON 4

**A. New Words.** Say each sound. Say each word.

1. b <u>i</u> b      J <u>i</u> m      b <u>a</u> d

2. h <u>a</u> m      d <u>i</u> d      D <u>a</u> d

3. p <u>a</u> d      h <u>a</u> t      b <u>i</u> g

4. d i p      h i t      m a t

5. g a s      h a s      h i s

Circle the word that goes with each picture.

1.     (bib)    Jim    bad

2.     ham    did    (Dad)

3.     pad    (hat)    big

4.     dip    hit    (mat)

5.     (gas)    has    his

■ **Sight Words.** Say the words.

with   no   go   she   my   to   water   on   little   was

■ **Challenge Words.** Say the words.

napkin   picnic   timid   zigzag   candid
1  2      1  2      1  2      1  2      1  2

**B.  Sentences and Stories.** Read each story. Write the story number under the picture that goes with each story.

**Story 1**

Jim <u>and</u> Dad had <u>a</u> picnic.
Jim and Dad sat <u>on</u> <u>a</u> big mat.
Dad had <u>a</u> napkin <u>and</u> Jim had <u>a</u> bib.

*2*

**Story 2**

Dad has <u>a</u> big van.
His van has <u>no</u> gas.
Can <u>a</u> van <u>go</u> <u>with</u> <u>no</u> gas?

*3*

**Story 3**

Sam <u>and</u> Nan <u>go</u> <u>to</u> <u>the</u> attic.
Nan has <u>a</u> big hat.
Sam has <u>a</u> <u>little</u> bat.

*1*

**C. Spelling.** Write the words and sentence that your teacher says.

1. _Did_  3. _mat_

2. _his_  4. _Jim_

5. _Dad has a big van ._

_____

**D. Practice Activity 1.** Fill in each blank with the best word.

| | | | | |
|---|---|---|---|---|
| 1. | The man ran to _his_ van. | (his) | has | hit |
| 2. | Jim and Dad _dip_ in the water. | big | pad | dip |
| 3. | Sam sat on my _mat_. | mat | six | sip |
| 4. | The _bib_ has a rip. | sit | bib | sip |
| 5. | A _ham_ is in the can. | tap | tan | ham |
| 6. | The school is _big_. | big | hit | did |
| 7. | A pin was in the _hat_. | fit | his | hat |
| 8. | Nan _has_ six maps. | ad | has | ham |
| 9. | Jim _did_ go to school. | did | big | hat |
| 10. | Dad has _gas_ in the van. | bad | gas | dip |

18

Correct

**E. Practice Activity 2.** Draw a line under the sentence that goes with each picture.

1. Dad and Jim go on a picnic.

 Dad and Jim go to the cabin.

2. Ham is in the can.

 Jim is in the hat.

3. Jim has a napkin.

 Jim has a bib.

4. Gas can go in the van.

 Gas can go in the can.

5. Nan has a big hat.

 Nan has a little pad.

6. The rabbit sits on the mat.

 The cat is in the bag.

7. The mat has a rip.

 The bib has a rip.

8. Did Sam hit with his bat?

 Did Nan dip in the water?

Correct ☐ Checking Up

19

# LESSON 5

■ **New Sound.** Say the word.

m<u>o</u>p

**A. New Words.** Say each sound. Say each word.

1. <u>o</u> n          <u>o</u> x          m <u>o</u> b

2. m <u>o</u> p          m <u>a</u> p          r <u>a</u> t

3. r <u>o</u> t          f <u>o</u> x          r <u>o</u> d

4. r i d          n o t          N a t

5. B o b          r i b          n o d

Circle the word that goes with each picture.

1.           on          (ox)          mob

2.           (mop)          map          rat

3.           rot          (fox)          rod

4.           rid          not          (Nat)

5.           (Bob)          rib          nod

■ **Sight Words.** Say the words.

after   of   from   to   with   people   water   he   school   my

■ **Challenge Words.** Say the words.

cannot   fossil   hatbox   madcap   mishap
1  2      1  2     1  2      1  2       1  2

**B.** **Sentences and Stories.** Read each story. Write the story number under the picture that goes with each story.

**Story 1**
Bob cannot go in a cab.
Bob can go in a van.
The people go in a van to school.

_3_

**Story 2**
The dog ran after the fox.
The fox ran to the water.
He ran from the dog.

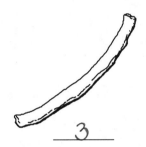

_1_

**Story 3**
The rib is a fossil.
The rib is from an ox.
The fossil cannot rot.

_2_

21

C. **Spelling.** Write the words and sentence that your teacher says.

1. Bob                    3. Nod

2. Map                    4. Mop

5. Bob has a mop


(D.) **Practice Activity 1.** Fill in each blank with the best word.

1. The fox __hid__ from the dog.                    hid      sat      cat

2. Bob can __mop__ the water.                       map      mop      mat

3. Gas can go in the __van__.                       six      van      mob

4. The dog __hid__.                                 his      hid      not

5. The cat is __not__ in the cabin.                 Nan      not      nod

6. The __map__ is in the cabin.                     map      did      not

7. The cat is __fat__.                              fin      fat      nod

8. The dog ran after the __cat__.                   mop      cat      rot

9. The ham cannot rot in a __can__.                 mad      not      can

10. Bob hid the __map__.                            ran      rid      map

Correct

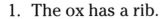

E. **Practice Activity 2.** Draw a line under the sentence that goes with each picture.

1. The ox has a rib.  <u>The rat has a hat.</u>

2. <u>Nan can mop the water.</u>  Nan can sip the water.

3. <u>The little hat is in the hatbox.</u>  The little pin is on the hatbox.

4. Bob ran after my dog.  <u>The dog ran after the fox.</u>

5. <u>Nat is mad.</u>  Nat is not mad.

6. <u>The man has a can with a lid.</u>  Bob has a mop.

7. <u>The ham can rot in a bag.</u>  <u>The ham cannot rot in a can.</u>

8. The mob of people hid.  <u>He hid the fan at school.</u>

☐ Correct

# LESSON 6

**A. New Words.** Say each sound. Say each word.

1.  B <u>o</u> b      j <u>o</u> b      l <u>o</u> t
2.  j <u>o</u> t      h <u>i</u> m      (b <u>o</u> x)
3.  c <u>a</u> b      (c <u>o</u> b)      h <u>o</u> t
4.  (t i p)      (h i t)      t o p
5.  d o t      h i p      h o p

Circle the word that goes with each picture.

1.  (Bob)      job      lot

2.  jot      him      (box)

3.  cab      (cob)      hot

4.  (tip)      (hit)      top

5.  dot      hip      (hop)

24

■ **Sight Words.** Say the words.

| some | of | with | after | from | was | school | to | go | she |
|------|-----|------|-------|------|-----|--------|-----|-----|-----|
| 6 | 4 | 10 | 1 | 2 | 9 | 2 | 8 | 3 | 5 |

■ **Challenge Words.** Say the words.

robin   avid   bobbin   canvas   catnap

| 1  2 | 1  2 | 1  2 | 1  2 | 1  2 |
|------|------|------|------|------|
| 5 | 1 | 2 | 3 | 6 |

**B. Sentences and Stories.** Read each story. Write the story number under the picture that goes with each story.

**Story 1**
Bob has a big box.
Some catnip is in the box.
Canvas is on the top.
The cat cannot go after the catnip.

3

**Story 2**
Pam has a job.
She is in a cab on the job.
People go with Pam.
The people tip Pam.

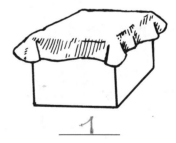

1

**Story 3**
The robin was in the lot.
She sat on a mat.
The mat was hot.
The robin did a hop.

2

**C. Spelling.** Write the words and sentence that your teacher says.

1. _Job_     3. _him_

2. _not_     4. _top_

5. _the pot was hot_

**D. Practice Activity 1.** Say the word. Fill in the blank with the word that has the same ending. Read the sentence.

1. **lot**
   The water is _hot_.          (job, hot)

2. **Bob**
   Sam sees Pam at her _Job_.          (job, nod)

3. **top**
   See the little rabbit _hop_.          (his, hop)

4. **fox**
   Some of the hats are in the _box_.          (bit, box)

5. **sit**
   With a bat, you can _hit_.          (hit, hat)

6. **lip**
   Nan hit her _hip_.          (hop, hip)

7. **hot**
   The canvas has a big _dot_.          (dot, him)

Correct

**E.** **Practice Activity 2.** Draw a line under the sentence that goes with each picture.

1. <u>A robin sat on a box.</u>          A cat ran to the catnip.

2. The box had a dot.          <u>The box had a top.</u>

3. Pam is in the lot.          <u>Pam is in the cab.</u>

4. <u>Bob can jot on a pad.</u>          Bob cannot hop on a pad.

5. The people ran from the ox.          <u>The people see a fox.</u>

6. Pam has a job.          <u>Sam and Nan ran to school.</u>

7. <u>The pot was hot.</u>          The can was hot.

8. <u>The dog hid the cob.</u>          The tip hit him on the hip.

Correct

27

# LESSON 7

**A. New Words.** Say each sound. Say each word.

| | | | | | | | | | |
|---|---|---|---|---|---|---|---|---|---|
| 1. | c <u>o</u> t | | c <u>a</u> t | | t <u>o</u> t |
| 2. | f <u>o</u> x | | j <u>o</u> g | | j <u>i</u> g |
| 3. | g <u>o</u> t | | s <u>o</u> p | | c <u>o</u> d |
| 4. | c a p | | n o t | | l o g |
| 5. | p a t | | p o t | | p i t |

Circle the word that goes with each picture.

1.  cot    (cat)    tot

2.  (fox)    jog    jig

3.  got    sop    (cod)

4.  (cap)    not    log

5.  pat    (pot)    pit

■ **Sight Words.** Say the words.

put    from    after    with    to    people    on    my    water    little

■ **Challenge Words.** Say the words.

tactic    mimic    comma    tonsil    cosmic
1  2    1  2    1  2    1  2    1  2

**B.** **Sentences and Stories.** Read each story. Write the story number under the picture that goes with each story.

**Story 1**
The timid cat sat on the cot.
The tot can mimic him.
The cat ran from the tot.
Can the tot jog after the cat?

2

**Story 2**
The little fox did a jig.
People ran after the fox.
The fox hid in a log.
It hid from the people.

3

**Story 3**
Pam got a big pot.
She put water in it.
The pot can tip.
The mop can sop the water.

1

**C. Spelling.** Write the words and sentence that your teacher says.

1. Cat                          3. pat

2. got                          4. not

5. Pam got a big pot.

---

**D. Practice Activity 1.** Fill in each blank with the best word.

1. The fox hid in a __pit__ .                    pit     pat     sit

2. The __fox__ was sad.                          fix     mix     fox

3. Six people __jog__ .                          jog     lip     bib

4. Bob and Sam __pat__ the cat.                  pot     pat     cab

5. The hat and __cap__ go in a box.              ran     mix     cap

6. Pam got a big __pot__ .                        not     pot     sop

7. Sam __got__ a big box.                        jog     got     jig

8. The rat ran from the __cat__ .                did     sat     cat

9. Pam has a __log__ cabin.                      hat     hit     log

10. People sit on a __cot__ .                     cot     sat     not

☐ Correct

**E. Practice Activity 2.** Draw a line under the sentence that goes with each picture.

1. <u>The lid cannot fit on the pot.</u>    The cod cannot fit in the pot.

2. Pat did a jig.    <u>The rat did a jig with the cat.</u>

3. <u>The tot has a little cap.</u>    My cap is in the hatbox.

4. <u>The fox hid in the pit.</u>    The tot pats the fox.

5. The cot is in the box.    <u>The cot is in the log cabin.</u>

6. The man can sip.    <u>The mop can sop the water.</u>

7. Dad got a job.    Nat <u>jogs to school</u>.

8. <u>The napkin has a rip.</u>  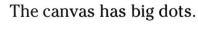  The canvas has big dots.

# LESSON 8

■ **New Sound.** Say the word.

r<u>u</u>g   

**A. New Words.** Say each sound. Say each word.

1. <u>u</u> p      <u>u</u> s      r <u>u</u> n

2. r <u>u</u> b      s <u>o</u> d      m <u>u</u> g

3. f <u>u</u> n      f <u>a</u> n      s <u>u</u> n

4. p i n      m u d      m a d

5. p u n      r u g      r i g

Circle the word that goes with each picture.

1.     up    us    (run)

2.     rub    sod    (mug)

3.     fun    (fan)    sun

4.     (pin)    mud    mad

5.     pun    (rug)    rig

■ **Sight Words.** Say the words.

they    very    have    from    little    water    he    people    and    on

■ **Challenge Words.** Say the words.

until    sunup    muffin    rustic    suntan
1 2      1 2      1 2       1 2       1 2

**B. Sentences and Stories.** Read each story. Write the story number under the picture that goes with each story.

**Story 1**
Sam <u>and</u> Pam <u>have</u> fun in <u>the</u> sun.
Sam has <u>a</u> suntan from <u>the</u> sun.
Pam sits <u>on a little</u> rug.
Sam runs in <u>the water</u>.

2

**Story 2**
Jim is in <u>the</u> mud.
<u>The</u> cat is in <u>the</u> mud.
Jim can rub mud <u>on the</u> cat.
<u>The</u> cat is <u>very</u> mad.

3

**Story 3**
<u>The</u> log cabin is rustic.
<u>The</u> cabin has <u>a</u> fan <u>and a</u> cot.
People picnic at <u>the</u> log cabin.
<u>They</u> sit <u>on the</u> sod.

1

## C. Spelling. Write the words and sentence that your teacher says.

1. _Run_      3. _fan_

2. _us_      4. _rug_

5. _The sun is up_

## D. Practice Activity 1. Say the word. Fill in the blank with the word that has the same ending. Read the sentence.

1. **run**
   The __sun__ is hot.         (sun, sat)

2. **rub**
   The dog is in the __tub__ .         (tub, tab)

3. **bug**
   The cat sat on a __rug__ .         (jig, rug)

4. **rug**
   Bob put water in the __mug__ .         (mug, mad)

5. **sun**
   Bob and Nat had __fun__ .         (fun, fan)

6. **fog**
   The fox hid in a __log__ .         (lip, log)

7. **jot**
   The __pot__ has a lid.         (pot, pat)

Correct

**E. Practice Activity 2.** Draw a line under the sentence that goes with each picture.

1. <u>Nan got a suntan.</u>    Nan got a pin.

2. Nat and Nan sit on a rug.    <u>Nat and Nan sit on a log.</u>

3. <u>The tot can run after the cat.</u>    The tot can rub the cat.

4. <u>Bob can see the fan.</u>    Bob can see us.

5. He can mix in a can.    <u>He can mix in a mug.</u>

6. <u>Kim was in the mud.</u>    Kim was very mad.

7. They have fun until sunup.    <u>They have six muffins.</u>

8. <u>The little cabin is rustic.</u>    The sun is up.

Correct　　　　　Checking Up　　　　35

# LESSON 9

**A. New Words.** Say each sound. Say each word.

1. b <u>u</u> d      b <u>i</u> d      b <u>u</u> t

2. c <u>u</u> b      c <u>a</u> b      t <u>u</u> b

3. c <u>u</u> p      c <u>o</u> d      h <u>u</u> t

4. n o t      n u t      h o t

5. b u s      d u g      d o g

Circle the word that goes with each picture.

1.    (bud)   bid   but

2.    cub   cab   (tub)

3.    (cup)   cod   hut

4.    not   (nut)   hot

5.    bus   dug   (dog)

■ **Sight Words.** Say the words.

saw     went     very     they     of     she     are     have     from     her

■ **Challenge Words.** Say the words.

public     ribbon     campus     hiccup     cotton
1   2      1   2      1   2      1   2      1   2

**B.  Sentences and Stories.** Read each story. Write the story number under the picture that goes with each story.

**Story 1**

Nan's dog <u>was</u> <u>on</u> <u>the</u> cotton mat.
<u>She</u> <u>put</u> <u>her</u> dog in <u>the</u> tub.
But <u>the</u> tub did not <u>have</u> water.
Nan got <u>water</u> <u>from</u> <u>the</u> tap.

2

**Story 2**

Tim <u>was</u> <u>on</u> <u>a</u> public bus.
<u>The</u> bus sat in <u>the</u> sun.
Tim got <u>very</u> hot.
<u>He</u> had <u>a</u> cup <u>of</u> <u>water</u>.

3

**Story 3**

At sunup, <u>the</u> cub got up.
<u>The</u> cub ran <u>to</u> <u>the</u> <u>water</u>.
<u>The</u> cub had <u>some</u> <u>water</u>.
<u>The</u> cub dug up <u>some</u> nuts.

1

**C.  Spelling.** Write the words and sentence that your teacher says.

1.  _But_____   3.  _bus_____

2.  _cap_____   4.  _cup_____

5.  _The sun is hot_____

_____

**D.  Practice Activity 1.** Fill in each blank with the best word.

1.  Pam went in a __cab__.        cat    cab    dog

2.  She has a __nut__.           nut    dug    mad

3.  The sun is very __hot__.      hut    hot    not

4.  People sit in the __bus__.    cup    mug    bus

5.  The __dog__ dug a pit.        hot    dog    bud

6.  We saw the __cub__.           us     dug    cub

7.  Hot water is in the __tub__.  bid    not    tub

8.  A rug is in the __hut__.      not    hut    nut

9.  Water is not in the __cup__.  cup    dug    us

10.  The __cod__ is in the pot.   hot    cod    bid

38                                                  Correct

**E.** **Practice Activity 2.** Draw a line under the sentence that goes with each picture.

1. The robin sat on a bud.    <u>The robin sat on a log.</u>

2. <u>The dogs are in the tub.</u>    The dogs are in the cab.

3. <u>Tim got on the public bus.</u>    Nan has a cotton cap.

4. Her cat dug a pit.    <u>Her cat sat on the rug.</u>

5. <u>Kim put a nut in the cup.</u>    Kim can pat the cub.

6. <u>The sun is very hot.</u>    The pot is very hot.

7. <u>He put the cod in the pot.</u>    He put the cod in the mug.

8. A rat ran from the hut.    <u>A rat hid in the box.</u>

# LESSON 10

**A. New Words.** Say each sound. Say each word.

| | | | | | | |
|---|---|---|---|---|---|---|
| 1. | h <u>u</u> g | | b <u>i</u> g | | b <u>u</u> g | |
| 2. | p <u>u</u> p | | t <u>u</u> g | | t <u>a</u> g | |
| 3. | h <u>u</u> m | | c <u>u</u> t | | h <u>a</u> m | |
| 4. | r u t | | b u n | | s u b | |
| 5. | s o b | | j u g | | r o t | |

Circle the word that goes with each picture.

1.   hug    big    (bug)

2.   (pup)    tug    tag

3.   hum    (cut)    ham

4.   rut    (bun)    sub

5.   (sob)    jug    rot

■ **Sight Words.** Say the words.

into   I   very   saw   some   they   go   from   after   with

■ **Challenge Words.** Say the words.

habit   submit   summit   vivid   comic
1   2    1   2    1   2    1   2    1   2

**B.  Sentences and Stories.** Read each story. Write the story number under the picture that goes with each story.

**Story 1**

Kit has a pup.

The pup is very little.

The pup fits into a hatbox.

Kit hugs the pup.

_____

**Story 2**

The tot had some fun.

The pup can run in the sun.

The tot ran after the pup.

Can the tot tag the pup?

_____

**Story 3**

Tom and Tim go on a picnic.

They have a jug of water.

They have some ham.

They sit and picnic at the summit.

_____

**C. Spelling.** Write the words and sentence that your teacher says.

1. Cut     3. hum

2. ham     4. hug

5. Nan will hug the pup.

**D. Practice Activity 1.** Say the word. Fill in the blank with the word that has the same ending. Read the sentence.

1. **hug**
   I saw a very big _bug_ .                    (not, bug)

2. **cup**
   A little dog is a _pup_ .                    (pup, mop)

3. **hot**
   The ham cannot _rot_ .                    (rot, rat)

4. **nut**
   Nat _cut_ the fabric.                    (sob, cut)

5. **mug**
   Put some water in the _jug_ .                    (jug, jig)

6. **sun**
   Nan has ham on a _bun_ .                    (bun, bit)

7. **tub**
   The _sub_ is in the water.                    (sub, sob)

Correct

**E.  Practice Activity 2.** Draw a line under the sentence that goes with each picture.

1. <u>The cat ran after the bug.</u>  The cat ran into the hut.

2. Tom has a jug of water.  <u>Tom has a pot of water.</u>

3. <u>Nan can hug Jim.</u>  Nan can hum.

4. <u>The bug sat in the sun.</u>  The bug is on the rug.

5. <u>The tan pup tugs at the rug.</u>  The tan pup sits in the rut.

6. He is at the summit.  <u>The sub is in the water.</u>

7. Dad has a big top hat.  <u>Jim has a little cap.</u>

8. The little tot sobs.  <u>The little tot sips from a cup.</u>

Correct

43

# LESSON 11

■ **New Sound.** Say the word.

n<u>e</u>t

**A. New Words.** Say each sound. Say each word.

| | | | | | |
|---|---|---|---|---|---|
| 1. | <u>E</u> d | f <u>e</u> d | s <u>e</u> t |
| 2. | s <u>i</u> t | m <u>e</u> n | r <u>e</u> d |
| 3. | n <u>o</u> t | l <u>e</u> d | l <u>a</u> d |
| 4. | w e b | m e t | l o t |
| 5. | l e t | g e t | r o d |

Circle the word that goes with each picture.

1.    (Ed)    fed    set

2.    sit    (men)    red

3.    not    (led)    lad

4.    (web)    met    lot

5.    let    get    (rod)

■ **Sight Words.** Say the words.

look    down    some    saw    very    they    after    was    little    from

■ **Challenge Words.** Say the words.

upset    exit    septic    sadden    panel
1  2    1 2    1  2    1  2    1  2

**B.** **Sentences and Stories.** Read each story. Write the story number under the picture that goes with each story.

**Story 1**
Ed fed his dog, Red.
Ed put some ham in a cup.
He let the dog go.
Red ran to the cup.

_3_

**Story 2**
Kit saw a red bug on a web.
She went after the bug.
She did not get the bug in her net.
Kit was very upset.

_1_

**Story 3**
Six men sit on the summit.
They look down from the top.
The men see people in a lot.
The people look little.

_2_

C. **Spelling.** Write the words and sentence that your teacher says.

1. _Fed_                    3. _lot_

2. _men_                    4. _get_

5. _Ed fed his dog ham_

_____

D. **Practice Activity 1.** Say the word. Fill in the blank with the word that has the same ending. Read the sentence.

1. **bed**
   The box has a ___red___ tag.                    (red, rot)

2. **Ben**
   The ___men___ ran.                    (met, men)

3. **met**
   Ed can ___get___ a cab.                    (get, set)

4. **bet**
   Ed ___set___ the box down.                    (set, get)

5. **met**
   Sam can ___get___ ham.                    (get, let)

6. **red**
   Jim ___led___ the dog.                    (led, lot)

7. **got**
   Jim did ___not___ go.                    (not, Nat)

46                                                        ☐ Correct

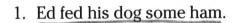

**E.** **Practice Activity 2.** Draw a line under the sentence that goes with each picture.

1. <u>Ed fed his dog some ham.</u>  Ed fed his dog a muffin.

2. Pat met six people.  <u>Pat led six pups.</u>

3. Kim has a red bib.  <u>Kim has a red hat.</u>

4. The men sit down.  <u>Tim sits on a box.</u>

5. <u>Ed let Nat have the rod.</u>  Ed let Nat have the cap.

6. Tim met Tom in the lot.  <u>Tim met Tom at the exit.</u>

7. <u>A big bug is in the web.</u>  The lad got six bugs.

8. Nan looks at the water.  <u>Nan looks at a map.</u>

Correct

# LESSON 12

**A. New Words.** Say each sound. Say each word.

1. g <u>e</u> t          p <u>e</u> t          h <u>e</u> m

2. b <u>e</u> d          h <u>u</u> m          p <u>e</u> n

3. p <u>a</u> n          l <u>e</u> g          l <u>o</u> g

4. l  u  g            b  e  t            b  a  t

5. t  e  n            j  e  t            j  o  t

Circle the word that goes with each picture.

1.           get          (pet)          hem

2.           (bed)          hum          pen

3.           pan          (leg)          log

4.           lug          bet          (bat)

5.           (ten)          jet          jot

48

■ **Sight Words.** Say the words.

where   children   some   see   very   my   with   on   water   I

■ **Challenge Words.** Say the words.

hectic   helmet   hidden   denim   puppet
  1  2     1  2      1  2     1  2      1  2

**B.  Sentences and Stories.** Read each story. Write the story number under the picture that goes with each story.

**Story 1**
Where is the pan hidden?
I cannot get my pet some water.
Is the pan in the tub?
I bet Ed fed my pet.

_1_

**Story 2**
Jan had a little puppet.
The puppet had denim legs.
Jan can get the puppet to jig.
I bet Jan can get the puppet to hum.

_3_

**Story 3**
Where is my red pen?
I see it on the bed.
It is not hidden.
I can jot with my pen.

_2_

**C. Spelling.** Write the words and sentence that your teacher says.

1. Pet

3. leg

2. pan

4. jet

5. The red pen is on the bed

**D. Practice Activity 1.** Change the underlined letter in each word to make another word. Write the letter on the line.

1. p _a_ t    ⟶      p _e_ t

2. l _u_ g    ⟶      l _o_ g

3. t _a_ n    ⟶      t _e_ n

4. j _o_ t    ⟶      j _e_ t

5. b _e_ t    ⟶      b _u_ t

Correct

**E.  Practice Activity 2.** Draw a line under the sentence that goes with each picture.

1.  <u>Jan can fix her hem.</u>                    Jan can jot with a red pen.

2.  Ed met some children.                    <u>Ed let the man in.</u>

3.  Nan set her pet on the log.              <u>Nan set her pet on the bed.</u>

4.  <u>Kit has a big puppet.</u>                    Kit has a red bag.

5.  <u>Nat can jog to school.</u>                  Nat can get very upset.

6.  Ten men get in a jet.                      <u>The man gets ten pens.</u>

7.  <u>The ham is in a pan.</u>                     The bun is in the pan.

8.  The bug has six legs.                      <u>I bet Sam can hum.</u>

☐ Correct                    ☐ Checking Up                    51

# LESSON 13

**A.** **New Words.** Say each sound. Say each word.

1. b <u>e</u> g          y <u>e</u> t          p <u>a</u> t

2. y <u>e</u> s          D <u>o</u> n          d <u>e</u> n

3. w <u>e</u> d          p <u>e</u> t          p <u>o</u> t

4. p i t          p e p          M o m

5. h e n          h i m          l e g

Circle the word that goes with each picture.

1.           beg          yet          (pat)

2.           yes          (Don)          den

3.           wed          pet          (pot)

4.           (pit)          pep          Mom

5.           (hen)          him          leg

52

■ **Sight Words.** Say the words.

work   said   where   saw   very   school   her   have   to   he

■ **Challenge Words.** Say the words.

rotten   comet   fatten   inlet   goblet
1  2     1  2     1  2     1  2     1  2

**B.  Sentences and Stories.** Read each story. Write the story number under the picture that goes with each story.

**Story 1**

Meg has a pet hen.
Meg led the hen to the pen.
She fed her pet.
Meg put her hen to bed.

2

**Story 2**

Where is the cub?
The cub is in a den.
The cub has hidden nuts in the den.
The cub can dig up the nuts.

3

**Story 3**

Don went to the summit.
He saw a very red comet.
"Yes, it was a comet," said Don.
The comet was little, yet Don saw it.

1

**C. Spelling.** Write the words and sentence that your teacher says.

1. _____    3. _____

2. _____    4. _____

5. _____

_____

**D. Practice Activity 1.** Fill in each blank with the best word.

1. Mom has a ___box___ .                    box      beg      ten

2. The ___pet___ ran.                        pot      pet      yes

3. Ed can _____ Nan.                     set      dug      (wed)

4. Don hit his _____ .                   (leg)    yet      him

5. Don can dig a _____ .                 (rug)    fan      pit

6. Sam is in the _____ .                 beg      (den)    pot

7. _____ the dog.                        Pot      (Pat)    Pit

8. The hen has _____ .                   (bus)    pep      den

9. _____ , I can hum.                    (Yes)    Pot      Pep

10. Mom will _____ to go.                pot      (beg)    leg

☐  Correct

**E. Practice Activity 2.** Draw a line under the sentence that goes with each picture.

1. The men get on a jet.  The men get in a van.

2. The red hen is in a pen.  The red hen is in a pit.

3. He has a pan of water.  He has a mug of water.

4. Ed sips from a goblet.  Ed dips in the pot.

5. Can Pat fatten her pet pig?  Where can Don see the comet?

6. The cub is in his den.  Mom is at work.

7. They have six pens.  They have six pets.

8. Meg met him at school.  Meg met him at the inlet.

Correct

# LESSON 14

■ **New Sound.** Say the words.

egg  o<u>ff</u>  hi<u>ll</u>  mi<u>ss</u>  mi<u>tt</u>  ja<u>zz</u>

**A. New Words.** Say each sound. Say each word.

| | | | | | | | | |
|---|---|---|---|---|---|---|---|---|
| 1. | o | <u>ff</u> | m | i | <u>ss</u> | m | i | <u>tt</u> |
| 2. | h | i | <u>ll</u> | m | a | <u>ss</u> | p | a | <u>ss</u> |
| 3. | l | e | <u>ss</u> | j | a | <u>zz</u> | k | i | <u>ss</u> |
| 4. | p | u | ff | p | u | tt | J | e | ff |
| 5. | e | gg | w | i | ll | f | i | ll |

Circle the word that goes with each picture.

1.   off  miss  mitt

2.  hill  mass  pass

3.   less  jazz  kiss

4.   puff  putt  Jeff

5.   egg  will  fill

56

■ **Sight Words.** Say the words.

be     play     saw     after     with     children     some     to     my     from

■ **Challenge Words.** Say the words.

sunset     kitten     eggnog     signal     velvet
1   2      1   2      1   2       1   2      1   2

**B.   Sentences and Stories.** Read each story. Write the story number under the picture that goes with each story.

**Story 1**
Don fills his cup <u>with</u> eggnog.
<u>He</u> has <u>to</u> get <u>a</u> napkin.
<u>The</u> kitten sips <u>from</u> <u>the</u> cup.
Don will <u>have</u> less eggnog.

_____

**Story 2**
Jeff ran off <u>with</u> <u>my</u> mitt.
<u>He</u> ran up <u>the</u> hill <u>with</u> <u>my</u> mitt.
<u>I</u> ran <u>after</u> him.
<u>I</u> got <u>my</u> mitt.

_____

**Story 3**
Lin has <u>a</u> pet cat, Velvet.
Velvet has a kitten.
Lin pets <u>the</u> kitten.
Will Lin kiss <u>the</u> kitten?

_____

**C. Spelling.** Write the words and sentence that your teacher says.

1. _____   3. _____

2. _____   4. _____

5. _____

_____

**D. Practice Activity 1.** Fill in each blank with the best word.

| less | egg | fill | will | jazz |
|------|------|------|------|------|
| hill | kiss | mitt | off | Jeff |

1. The men jog up the _____.

2. The lid is _____ the pan.

3. Jeff _____ fill the pan.

4. Pam will have ham and an _____.

5. Nan has a bat and a _____.

6. Jan can _____ the pot with water.

7. Lin will _____ the kitten.

8. Don plays _____ after school.

9. Where is _____?

10. Six is _____ than ten.

Correct

**E. Practice Activity 2.** Draw a line under the sentence that goes with each picture.

1. An egg and a ham are in the pan.  An egg and a bun are in the pot.

2. The pup jogs up the hill.  The pup is led up the hill.

3. The cat is in the bed.  Velvet will be with her kitten.

4. Ed fills the mug with eggnog.  Ed fills the box with hats.

5. Jan will pass him in the cab.  Jan will miss the children.

6. Jeff ran off with my mitt.  Lin will kiss her cat.

7. Don saw a mass of people.  Don saw a comet.

8. Fill the can with some eggs.  Fill the pot with some water.

Correct

# LESSON 15

**A. New Words.** Say each sound. Say each word.

1. B i <u>ll</u>     h u <u>ff</u>     d i <u>ll</u>

2. d o <u>ll</u>     l e <u>ss</u>     l o <u>ss</u>

3. f u <u>ss</u>     m e <u>ss</u>     h i <u>ss</u>

4. J i ll     m u tt     b o ss

5. f i ll     B e ss     f e ll

Circle the word that goes with each picture.

1.      Bill     huff     dill

2.      doll     less     loss

3.      fuss     mess     hiss

4.      Jill     mutt     boss

5.      fill     Bess     fell

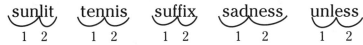

- **Sight Words.** Say the words.

  tree  snow  with  children  after  see  they  very  be  she

- **Challenge Words.** Say the words.

  sunlit    tennis    suffix    sadness    unless
  1   2     1   2     1   2     1   2      1   2

**B.   Sentences and Stories.** Read each story. Write the story number under the picture that goes with each story.

**Story 1**

Bill and Bess sit in a sunlit cabin.
They see a very big mess in the cabin.
Dad will fuss at the mess.
Get a can and fill it up!

_____

**Story 2**

Jill fell down.
Her satin dress was a mess.
The satin fabric had a rip.
Jill was very upset.

_____

**Story 3**

Lin will play tennis with Jan.
Lin will huff and puff.
Jan will not win.
Will Jan be upset at the loss?

_____

**C. Spelling.** Write the words and sentence that your teacher says.

1. _____   3. _____

2. _____   4. _____

5. _____

_____

**D. Practice Activity 1.** Fill in each blank with the best word.

| doll | ten | kitten | Bill | egg |
| boss | kiss | sunup | mug | fox |

1. Jill and _____ sat in the cabin.

2. Bess will play with a _____.

3. Mom will fill the _____.

4. Jan is Bill's _____ on the job.

5. Mom and Dad have _____ children.

6. The hen sat on an _____.

7. Dad will _____ Mom.

8. The red _____ ran down the hill.

9. Jeff and Bess got up at _____.

10. The cat had a _____.

Correct

**E.** **Practice Activity 2.** Draw a line under the sentence that goes with each picture.

1. The box fell off the cot. The doll fell off the bed.

2. Bill fed the mutt. The cat will hiss at the mutt.

3. Bess plays with her mitt. Bess plays with her doll.

4. The hut is a big mess. The cabin is on the hill.

5. The little kitten is in the tree. The little pup is in the tree.

6. Jeff will fill the can with dill. Jeff will fill the pan with eggs.

7. Her boss will fuss at the loss. Amy fills the hatbox with hats.

8. The children play in the snow. The children play tennis.

Correct

# LESSON 16

**A.** **New Words.** Say each sound. Say each word.

| | | | | | | | | | |
|---|---|---|---|---|---|---|---|---|---|
| 1. | l | a | <u>ss</u> | h | i | <u>ll</u> | l | e | <u>ss</u> |
| 2. | g | i | <u>ll</u> | l | o | <u>ss</u> | J | e | <u>ss</u> |
| 3. | B | e | <u>ss</u> | o | <u>ff</u> | | m | o | <u>ss</u> |
| 4. | m | i | ss | t | o | ss | d | o | ll |
| 5. | f | i | ll | J | e | ff | b | o | ss |

Circle the word that goes with each picture.

1.      lass     hill     less

2.      gill     loss     Jess

3.      Bess     off     moss

4.     miss     toss     doll

5.     fill     Jeff     boss

■ **Sight Words.** Say the words.

went    said    with    play    snow    after    school    put    on    have

■ **Challenge Words.** Say the words.

tomcat    bellhop    bonnet    offset    hilltop
 1   2     1   2      1   2     1   2     1   2

**B.  Sentences and Stories.** Read each story. Write the story number
under the picture that goes with each story.

### Story 1

Jan had on a velvet bonnet.

Don had on a top hat.

A bellhop got a cab.

Jan and Don went off in the cab.

_____

### Story 2

Jess, my big tomcat, sat on a sunlit hilltop.

A mutt ran up to play with Jess.

Jess said, "Hiss!"

The mutt ran off.

I bet the mutt will not miss Jess!

_____

### Story 3

Bess plays with her doll after school.

She puts a little bonnet on her doll.

She fills cups with water.

Bess and her doll have a picnic.

_____

65

**C. Spelling.** Write the words and sentence that your teacher says.

1. _____   3. _____

2. _____   4. _____

5. _____

_____

**D. Practice Activity 1.** Fill in each blank with the best word.

| | | | | |
|---|---|---|---|---|
| 1. | Bess has a _____. | beg | ten | doll |
| 2. | The mutt ran up the _____. | pot | hill | loss |
| 3. | Jess can _____ the bat. | wed | loss | toss |
| 4. | Don will _____ his mutt. | moss | miss | fill |
| 5. | The _____ has a doll. | Jess | fill | lass |
| 6. | The _____ will fuss. | Jeff | fill | boss |
| 7. | Jeff will miss his _____. | pet | off | pit |
| 8. | Bess _____ down the hill. | fell | miss | den |
| 9. | I will get _____ ham. | fuss | loss | less |
| 10. | We see _____ on the hill. | moss | fill | gill |

Correct

**E.  Practice Activity 2.** Draw a line under the sentence that goes with each picture.

1.  The bonnet is on the little lass.     The bonnet is on the kitten.

2.  Lin will fill the pan with water.     Lin will fill the box with eggs.

3.  Moss is on the hill.     Moss is on the log.

4.  The hat fell off the bed.     The doll fell off the bed.

5.  Jeff can toss the nut.     Jeff can toss the mitt.

6.  Bess is ill and will miss school.     Jess is my tomcat.

7.  Jill is upset at the loss.     My boss saw moss on the hill.

8.  The tot sat with her doll.     The tot plays in the snow.

# LESSON

■ **New Sounds.** Say the words.

ro<u>ck</u>   pa<u>th</u>   di<u>sh</u>

**A. New Words.** Say each sound. Say each word.

1.  m  a  <u>th</u>      n  e  <u>ck</u>      N  i  <u>ck</u>

2.  p  a  <u>ck</u>      p  a  <u>th</u>      c  a  <u>sh</u>

3.  p  e  <u>ck</u>      b  a  <u>th</u>      f  i  <u>sh</u>

4.  r  o  ck        d  i  sh        m  o  th

5.  d  a  sh        J  a  ck        r  a  ck

Circle the word that goes with each picture.

1.        math      neck      Nick

2.        pack      path      cash

3.        peck      bath      fish

4.        rock      dish      moth

5.        dash      Jack      rack

■ **Sight Words.** Say the words.
down  went  play  where  water  some  saw  from  put  after

■ **Challenge Words.** Say the words.

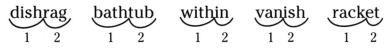
dishrag  bathtub  within  vanish  racket
 1  2     1  2     1  2    1  2     1  2

**B.  Sentences and Stories.** Read each story. Write the story number under the picture that goes with each story.

### Story 1:  The Fish

Jack went down the path. He went to the inlet to fish. He saw fish play in the water. He saw the fish vanish within the rocks. Jack got the rod from his pack. Will Jack get his limit of six fish?

_____

### Story 2:  The Mishap

Jack sat on a rock. He put the rod in the water. Where are the fish? At sunset, a fish bit. The fish was a big bass. Jack went after the fish with a net. He fell off the rock into the water. He did not get that fish.

_____

### Story 3:  After School

Nick plays tennis after school. He gets the racket from his bag. He runs and huffs. After Nick plays tennis, he is a mess. Nick is hot and will dash for the bathtub. He will fill the bathtub with water. He will get his legs and neck wet.

_____

**C.  Spelling.** Write the words and sentence that your teacher says.

1. _____     3. _____

2. _____     4. _____

5. _____

_____

**D.  Practice Activity.** Say the word. Fill in the blank with the word that has the same ending. Read the sentence.

1. **math**

   Jill jogs on the _____.                         (path, peck)

2. **path**

   The mutt will have a _____ in the tub.          (bath, boss)

3. **Jack**

   Nick put the racket in his _____.               (path, pack)

4. **pack**

   Meg put the dishrag on the _____.               (rock, rack)

5. **cash**

   Nat can _____ down the path.                    (doll, dash)

6. **dash**

   The _____ is in the box.                        (cash, Jack)

7. **bath**

   Jack will work on his _____.                    (math, miss)

Correct

E. **Practice Activity 2.** Draw a line under the sentence that goes with each picture.

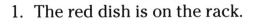

1. The red dish is on the rack.

The red dishrag is on the rack.

2. A moth is within the net.

A fish is within the net.

3. Bess plays with the tennis racket.

Bess plays with her doll.

4. Nick will toss a rock into the water.

Mom will fill the bathtub.

5. The tomcat will dash down the path.

Dad will pack the van.

6. Jack gets a fish.

The tot gets a bath.

7. The hen can peck at the tree.

The hen can peck at the mutt.

8. Jill has math at school.

Jill has a fish on the dish.

▢ Correct

# LESSON 18

**A. New Words.** Say each sound. Say each word.

1. p a <u>th</u>     b a <u>ck</u>     h u <u>sh</u>

2. w i <u>sh</u>     w i <u>th</u>     t a <u>ck</u>

3. b a <u>th</u>     m a <u>sh</u>     k i <u>ck</u>

4. t u ck     c a sh     r u sh

5. r a sh     l o ck     l u ck

Circle the word that goes with each picture.

1. path       back       hush

2. wish       with       tack

3. bath       mash       kick

4. tuck       cash       rush

5. rash       lock       luck

■ **Sight Words.** Say the words.

children   into   went   play   some   school   of   with   he   to

■ **Challenge Words.** Say the words.

backlog   backpack   packet   punish   ticket
  1    2      1    2       1    2      1    2      1    2

**B.** **Sentences and Stories.** Read each story. Write the story number under the picture that goes with each story.

**Story 1:  The School Bus**

   The children got on the school bus. They did not rush. Jeff had a backpack. Jeff and some of the children sat in the back of the bus. The man got the children to hush. The children got off the bus at school.

_____

**Story 2:  The Bath**

   Mom fills the bathtub. The tot runs. Mom has to rush after the tot. The tot has a rock. Will he toss the rock into the bathtub? The tot gets a bath. Mom tucks the tot into bed.

_____

**Story 3:  The Ticket**

   Jack has luck. He got a ticket to the school play. He had to dash to get the ticket. Lin will miss the play. She has a rash. Will Nick wish to go with Jack?

_____

C. **Spelling.** Write the words and sentence that your teacher says.

1. _____   3. _____

2. _____   4. _____

5. _____

_____

D. **Practice Activity 1.** Fill in each blank with the best word.

| back | rush | hush | kick | wish |
|------|------|------|------|------|
| path | tuck | lock | bath | with |

1. Jan will _____ the cash in a box.

2. Jack will _____ the rock.

3. The tot will get a _____ in the bathtub.

4. Jeff has a rash on his _____.

5. The dog will run down a _____.

6. The cat will _____ up the tree.

7. Dad will tell the children to _____.

8. Bess will _____ her doll in bed.

9. Can we go _____ Nat?

10. The children _____ it was sunset.

74

Correct

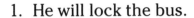

**E.  Practice Activity 2.** Draw a line under the sentence that goes
with each picture.

1.  He will lock the bus.          The children sit in the back.

2.  Bess gets the moth
    with a net.                    Bess put the doll in the bath.

3.  Nat put the tack in a box.          Nat will rush to school.

4.  The man got a packet
    of tickets.                    Jill has cash to get
                                                        the tickets.

5.  Tom went down the path.          Tom has a rash on his neck.

6.  The dog will get a bath.          Pat will kick the rock.

7.  The racket is in the backpack.          The dishrag is on the rack.

8.  Dad will tuck us into bed.          Will Mom punish the children?

[ ] Correct

# LESSON 19

**A. New Words.** Say each sound. Say each word.

1.  d  u  <u>ck</u>        d  o  <u>ck</u>        b  a  <u>th</u>

2.  p  a  <u>th</u>        d  e  <u>ck</u>        s  a  <u>ck</u>

3.  m  a  <u>sh</u>        s  o  <u>ck</u>        m  e  <u>sh</u>

4.  s  a  sh         t  a  ck         m  u  sh

5.  l  i  ck         p  i  ck         g  u  sh

Circle the word that goes with each picture.

1.     duck        dock        bath

2.     path        deck        sack

3.     mash        sock        mesh

4.     sash        tack        mush

5.    lick        pick        gush

■ **Sight Words.** Say the words.

down    went    play    she    water    saw    into    with    after    to

■ **Challenge Words.** Say the words.

backup    polish    publish    bucket    hammock

  1  2     1  2     1  2     1  2     1    2

**B.** **Sentences and Stories.** Read each story. Write the story number under the picture that goes with each story.

### Story 1: Jan

It was sunup. I was on the deck of the cabin. I saw Jan go down the path to the dock. I saw her toss a rock into the water and play with the ducks. After she fed the ducks, Jan went back down the path to the cabin.

_____

### Story 2: The Duck

I was in a hammock on the deck. I saw a tan duck on the dock. The duck saw a fish vanish into the water. The fish was a bass. The duck fell off the dock into the water. The duck got a bath.

_____

### Story 3: Mud on the Van

The van is a mess. It has mud on the top and on the back. I will fill a bucket with water. A sock can be a rag. The van will get a bath. I will rub off the mud and polish the van.

_____

**C. Spelling.** Write the words and sentence that your teacher says.

1. _____    3. _____

2. _____    4. _____

5. _____

_____

**D. Practice Activity 1.** Fill in each blank with the best word.

| bath | deck | polish | sash | lick |
|------|------|--------|------|------|
| tack | bucket | path | mash | pick |

1.  Nick went down the _____ and into the school.

2.  Bess will play on the _____ by the water.

3.  Mom put on the red _____.

4.  Jan sat on a big _____.

5.  The pet will _____ Jack's leg.

6.  Nick put the hen's eggs in a _____.

7.  You can _____ the goblet with a cotton rag.

8.  Do not _____ the rock with the bat.

9.  Jeff will _____ Bess to play after school.

10. The duck went for a _____ in the water.

Correct

**E. Practice Activity 2.** Draw a line under the sentence that goes with each picture.

1. Tom will fill the bucket with water.  Tom will fill the sack with tacks.

2. The dog has a bath in the tub.  The duck has a bath in the tub.

3. Nan has on a red sash.  Nan has on a tan sock.

4. The pup will lick the dish.  The duck is on the dock.

5. Rick will tack it up.  Rick will pick up the sack.

6. Tim will pick a dog.  Tim will dash down the path.

7. Jill sat on the dock.  Jill sat on the hammock.

8. The water will gush into the bucket.  Jan will polish the van.

Correct

# LESSON 20

■ **New Sounds.** Say the words.

ne<u>st</u> 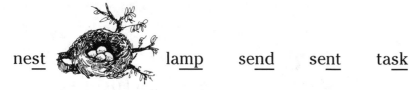 la<u>mp</u>  se<u>nd</u>  se<u>nt</u>  ta<u>sk</u>

**A. New Words.** Say each sound. Say each word.

1.  r  u  <u>st</u>      f  a  <u>st</u>      b  u  <u>mp</u>

2.  l  e  <u>nd</u>      l  e  <u>nt</u>      m  a  <u>sk</u>

3.  l  i  <u>st</u>      r  e  <u>st</u>      l  u  <u>mp</u>

4.  l  o  st       m  e  nd       l  a  mp

5.  h  a  nd       h  i  nt       a  sk

Circle the word that goes with each picture.

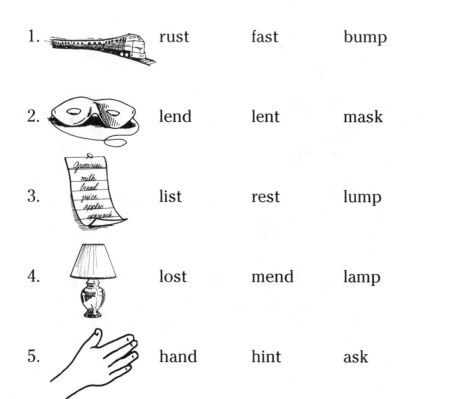

1.   rust      fast      bump

2.   lend      lent      mask

3.   list      rest      lump

4.   lost      mend      lamp

5.   hand      hint      ask

■ **Sight Words.** Say the words.

down    went    work    put    from    very    into    of    be    was

■ **Challenge Words.** Say the words.

insist    absent    picket    backrest    invest

1   2     1   2     1   2     1   2     1   2

**B.**   **Sentences and Stories.** Read each story. Write the story number under the picture that goes with each story.

**Story 1: The Lost Rack**

    Pam had a red van. She lent the van to Nick. Nick hit a lump of mud. The rack fell off the top of the van. It fell into the water. The rack is lost. It will rust in the water.

**Story 2: The Job**

    Mom is at work. She mends lamps. Mom puts tacks on the lamps. She can fix the lamps fast. Her boss will insist that Mom get rest. Mom will ask to be absent from work.

**Story 3: The Mask**

    Rick has a big velvet mask. He put the mask on his fat cat. The cat was hidden. Jack did not see the cat's neck. Did the cat vanish?

**C. Spelling.** Write the words and sentence that your teacher says.

1. _____  3. _____

2. _____  4. _____

5. _____

_____

**D. Practice Activity 1.** Fill in each blank with the best word.

| | | | | |
|------|------|------|------|------|
| lamp | mend | fast | lent | rest |
| rust | mask | ask | lost | list |

1. Ed will _____ the rip.

2. Mom lit the gas _____.

3. The old tin can has _____.

4. I will _____ to sit on the hammock.

5. Tom _____ Bill his backpack.

6. Meg has on a big _____.

7. The bus cannot go _____.

8. Jeff _____ his mitt.

9. She sat with the _____ of the children.

10. He has a _____ of the people in his school.

☐ Correct

**E.** **Practice Activity 2.** Draw a line under the sentence that goes with each picture.

1. The hammock had a backrest.  I can polish the lamp.

2. The red van went down the hill. 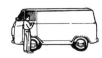 Tom can lock the red van.

3. Bill will rest on the cot.  Bill will lend Sam his backpack.

4. Jill had on a mask.  Bess has a mesh bag.

5. Nick lent Jan a tennis racket.  Nick lost the fish.

6. Mom will mend the sack. Kim will get her neck wet.

7. The can has rust.  The mat has a lump.

8. Dad had a very big list.  Dad had a bucket of fish.

Correct

# LESSON 21

**A. New Words.** Say each sound. Say each word.

| | | | | | | | | | | | |
|---|---|---|---|---|---|---|---|---|---|---|---|
| 1. | n | e | <u>st</u> | | l | a | <u>mp</u> | | m | u | <u>st</u> |
| 2. | l | a | <u>st</u> | | b | u | <u>mp</u> | | f | i | <u>st</u> |
| 3. | s | e | <u>nt</u> | | c | a | <u>st</u> | | s | e | <u>nd</u> |
| 4. | d | e | sk | | w | e | nt | | f | u | nd |
| 5. | s | a | nd | | m | a | sk | | m | i | nt |

Circle the word that goes with each picture.

1.    nest      lamp      must

2.    last      bump      fist

3.    sent      cast      send

4.    desk      went      fund

5.    sand      mask      mint

■ **Sight Words.** Say the words.

for    she    down    very    children    they    into    look    have    see

■ **Challenge Words.** Say the words.

disgust    contest    discuss    pocket    jackpot
1    2      1    2      1    2      1    2      1    2

**B.  Sentences and Stories.** Read each story. Write the story number under the picture that goes with each story.

**Story 1:  The Lost Fish**

The men went to the inlet to fish for bass. They set the big bucket down on a rock. The men put the bass in the bucket. The bucket fell into the water. The men lost the fish. The men got very wet and upset.

_____

**Story 2:  The Hen's Nest**

Look at the hen's nest. See the lump in the nest. The lump is an egg. We cannot pick up the egg. The hen will be sad. Hush! We must let the hen get back into the nest.

_____

**Story 3:  Jackpot**

Bess and Pat have contest tickets. The children wish to win the cash in the contest fund. They must have luck to win. Will they hit the jackpot? Will they have the best tickets? I bet they will have fun.

_____

**C. Spelling.** Write the words and sentence that your teacher says.

1. _____   3. _____

2. _____   4. _____

5. _____

_____

**D. Practice Activity 1.** Read each group of words. The groups of words are not in the correct order. Change the order of the words to make a sentence. Write each sentence on the line. Read each sentence.

1. will dig     Kit and Nat     in the sand

_____

2. in the nest     The egg     will fit

_____

3. Tom     the box     will send

_____

4. Bess     the jackpot     will win

_____

5. on the dock     The bucket     sits

_____

6. will sit     at his desk     Bob

_____

Correct

**E.** **Practice Activity 2.** Draw a line under the sentence that goes with each picture.

1. The men fell off the rock.  The man sat on the hammock.

2. Tom must mend the net.  Tom has a cast on his leg.

3. Dad sent Jan a velvet hat.  The children got six tickets.

4. The bellhop picks up the bags.  Bill puts rocks in the box.

5. They have fun in the sand.  They had ham with mint.

6. Rick has cash in his pocket.  The contest fund has cash.

7. The mask will fit Tom.  The lamp will fit in the box.

8. Nan had a puppet on her fist.  Did she sell the last fish?

Correct

# LESSON 22

**A. New Words.** Say each sound. Say each word.

| | | | | | | | | | |
|---|---|---|---|---|---|---|---|---|---|
| 1. | j | u | <u>mp</u> | p | u | <u>mp</u> | b | a | <u>nd</u> |
| 2. | h | a | <u>nd</u> | t | e | <u>nt</u> | r | a | <u>mp</u> |
| 3. | m | e | <u>nd</u> | d | u | <u>st</u> | d | u | <u>sk</u> |
| 4. | v | a | st | t | u | sk | t | a | sk |
| 5. | w | i | nd | p | o | nd | h | u | sk |

Circle the word that goes with each picture.

1.     jump      pump      band

2.     hand      tent      ramp

3.     mend      dust      dusk

4.     vast      tusk      task

5.    wind      pond      husk

■ **Sight Words.** Say the words.

work   down   she   play   from   see   into   look   of   he

■ **Challenge Words.** Say the words.

dentist   intend   invent   sandbox   locket
1   2      1   2    1   2     1    2      1   2

**B.   Sentences and Stories.** Read each story. Write the story number under the picture that goes with each story.

**Story 1:  Sand**

Tim went to the pond to rest. He sat down in the sand. Tim sat in the wind. The sand got on his hand and on his back. Tim ran down the ramp to the dock. Will Tim jump into the pond?

_____

**Story 2:  Pug and the Dog Contest**

Lin and Pug went to the dog contest. Lin saw a man look at the dogs. Pug did not sit down. Lin saw Pug jump up and lick the man. The rest of the pups did not get up and play. The man sent Pug and Lin from the contest. Pug did not win.

_____

**Story 3:  The Band**

The people sit in the vast tent. The band will play at dusk. Jill has a task. She pumps water into cups. The people sip from the cups. The man signals the band to play. The people hush.

_____

**C. Spelling.** Write the words and sentence that your teacher says.

1. _____   3. _____

2. _____   4. _____

5. _____

_____

**D. Practice Activity 1.** Change the first letter in each word to make another word that has the same ending sound. Write the letter on the line.

1. <u>p</u> u m p  ➡    _____ ump

2. <u>b</u> a n d  ➡    _____ and

3. <u>h</u> u s k  ➡    _____ usk

4. <u>l</u> a m p  ➡  _____ amp

5. <u>s</u> a n d  ➡  _____ and

☐ Correct

**E.** **Practice Activity 2.** Draw a line under the sentence that goes with each picture.

1. Don pumps gas into the van.  The duck is in the pond.

2. The pup can lick my hand.  The pup will jump into the sandbox.

3. The children look at the tusk. The children went to bed at dusk.

4. We cannot see the sun at dusk.  I must dust the lamp.

5. Jill has a task at her job.  Bill will rip the husks off.

6. Rick put a rock on his desk.  An egg is in the nest.

7. Jeff sent Nan a locket.  Jess must sit in the hammock.

8. The people sit in the vast tent.  Will the band win the contest?

# LESSON 23

**A. New Words.** Say each sound. Say each word.

1.  r  i  <u>sk</u>          t  e  <u>st</u>          w  e  <u>st</u>

2.  d  e  <u>sk</u>          l  a  <u>nd</u>          b  e  <u>st</u>

3.  b  e  <u>nt</u>          d  a  <u>mp</u>          r  a  <u>mp</u>

4.  b  u  mp          f  a  st          p  e  st

5.  p  a  st          l  u  mp          p  o  nd

Circle the word that goes with each picture.

1.      risk        test        west

2.      desk        land        best

3.      bent        damp        ramp

4.      bump        fast        pest

5.      past        lump        pond

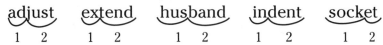

■ **Sight Words.** Say the words.

work she down where children they have into be look

■ **Challenge Words.** Say the words.

adjust   extend   husband   indent   socket
1   2     1   2      1   2      1   2      1   2

**B.** **Sentences and Stories.** Read each story. Write the story number under the picture that goes with each story.

### Story 1: The Pest

Lin has a pet ram. Lin's ram is a big pest. Lin led the ram to a ramp. Lin bent down to adjust the ramp. The ram ran past Lin. Will the ram bump Lin? Will it go up the ramp into the van?

_____

### Story 2: At Dusk

At dusk, Nan will jog. She will run on the sand at the pond. Nan will jog past the ducks. She will not run fast. She will not rush. Nan will look at the red sunset in the west.

_____

### Story 3: No Water

Tim had the best land in the west. His land was vast. Yet the land did not have a bit of water. The pond was not wet. The pond was just dust. The water pump did not work. Where will Tim and his children go? They must get water.

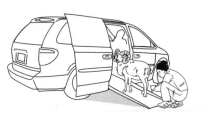

_____

C. **Spelling.** Write the words and sentence that your teacher says.

1. _____ 3. _____

2. _____ 4. _____

5. _____

_____

D. **Practice Activity 1.** Fill in each blank with the best word.

| | | west | test | pest |
|---|---|---|---|---|
| 1. | His land was in the _____. | west | test | pest |
| 2. | Jess was the _____ in the contest. | bump | best | past |
| 3. | The little pup must be a _____. | bent | pest | past |
| 4. | The ship will _____ at the dock. | land | lump | west |
| 5. | Nan ran _____ Jan on the path. | west | pet | past |
| 6. | The red van went up the _____. | ram | ramp | pet |
| 7. | Ants can be a _____ to a picnic. | ramp | risk | bet |
| 8. | Sam had a _____ in school. | test | west | bent |
| 9. | The children ran very _____. | jump | fast | last |
| 10. | Can he dust off his _____? | land | damp | desk |

Correct

**E.   Practice Activity 2.** Draw a line under the sentence that goes with each picture.

1.  The ram ran past Nan
    on the path.

    The ram ran up the ramp.

2.  My pet was the best pup
    in the contest.

    The man bent down to pet
    the pup.

3.  At dusk, the sun sets
    in the west.

    The children had a test.

4.  The mat has a lump.

    The log has a bump.

5.  The land extends
    into the water.

    We sat on rocks in the water.

6.  Pam got wet in the pond.

    Pam will fish in the pond.

7.  Her husband can fix
    the socket.

    Her husband is a dentist.

8.  The little egg will fit
    in his hand.

    I bet I can win the contest.

Correct

# LESSON 24

■ **New Sounds.** Say the words.

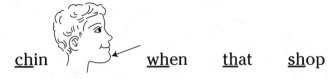

<u>ch</u>in        <u>wh</u>en        <u>th</u>at        <u>sh</u>op

**A.  New Words.** Say each sound. Say each word.

1.  <u>wh</u> e  n            <u>sh</u> i  p            <u>ch</u> i  p

2.  <u>ch</u> a  t            <u>th</u> a  t            <u>sh</u> e  d

3.  <u>th</u> i  s            <u>th</u> u  s            <u>ch</u> o  p

4.  wh i  p            sh o  p            th e  n

5.  wh i  z            ch i  n            th u  d

Circle the word that goes with each picture.

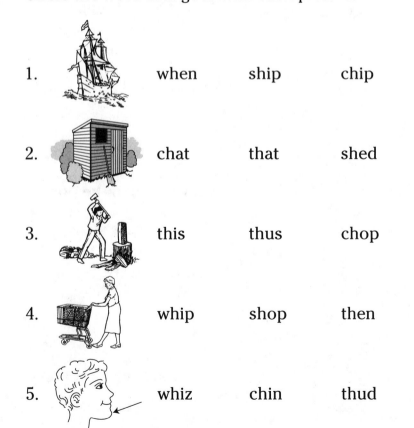

1.          when        ship        chip

2.          chat        that        shed

3.          this        thus        chop

4.          whip        shop        then

5.          whiz        chin        thud

■ **Sight Words.** Say the words.

work    down    children    tree    said    into    he    to    from    saw

■ **Challenge Words.** Say the words.

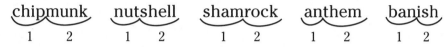

chipmunk    nutshell    shamrock    anthem    banish

1   2     1   2     1   2     1   2     1   2

**B.** **Sentences and Stories.** Read each part of the story. Write the story part number under the picture that goes with each story part.

## Ben and the Chipmunk

### Part 1

Chip, the little chipmunk, sat in his nest. His wish was to fill his nest with nuts. He ran down the tree. When he hit land, he ran down the path to the shed. In the shed, he got his pick of the best nuts in the box. He ran back to the tree and up to the nest. Then Chip fit the nuts into his nest.

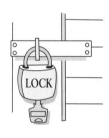

### Part 2

After work, Ben went to the shed to get nuts. Ben saw Chip vanish down the path. Ben said, "That chipmunk is a pest. He gets the best nuts. I will banish that chipmunk from this shed. He will have to get nuts from the tree."

### Part 3

At dusk, Chip ran back to the shed to get nuts. He dug in the box and got the best nuts. HUSH! THUD. THUD. THUD. Ben was in the shed. When Chip saw Ben, he ran very fast down the path. Ben put a lock on the shed. Thus, Chip cannot go back to the shed. He must get nuts from the tree.

**C. Spelling.** Write the words and sentence that your teacher says.

1. _____    3. _____

2. _____    4. _____

5. _____

_____

**D. Practice Activity 1.** Read each group of words. The groups of words are not in the correct order. Change the order of the words to make a sentence. Write each sentence on the line. Read each sentence.

1. will not get    into the shed    That chipmunk

_____

2. will dock    in the inlet    The ship

_____

3. has    a little chip    The dish

_____

4. will whip    Jeff    the eggs

_____

5. Mom got    from the dentist    a bill

_____

6. on the rock    hit his chin    Tim

_____

Correct

E. **Practice Activity 2.** Draw a line under the sentence that goes with each picture.

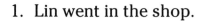

1. Lin went in the shop.　　　　Lin is in the shed.

2. The duck is in the sandbox.　　The tot will sit in the sandbox.

3. The dish has a big chip.　　　　The cup has a little chip.

4. Ed sells the best fish.　　　　The shop sells shamrocks.

5. That ship is at the dock.　　　　This ship is in the inlet.

6. It will whiz past the children.　　This chipmunk will dash up the tree.

7. Her husband will get some chops.　　Her husband will chat with them.

8. When it was dusk, Pam went to the pond.　　When the sun set, Pam went to the shop.

# LESSON 25

**A. New Words.** Say each sound. Say each word.

| | | | | |
|---|---|---|---|---|
| 1. | <u>sh</u> e d | <u>th</u> i s | <u>sh</u> o p |
| 2. | <u>th</u> a t | <u>th</u> i n | <u>ch</u> i n |
| 3. | <u>sh</u> i p | <u>ch</u> a p | <u>ch</u> a t |
| 4. | wh i p | ch u g | ch i p |
| 5. | th e n | sh u t | wh e n |

Circle the word that goes with each picture.

1.      shed     this     shop

2.      that     thin     chin

3.      ship     chap     chat

4.      whip     chug     chip

5.      then     shut     when

■ **Sight Words.** Say the words.

go   down   to   work   they   some   from   into   see   water

---

■ **Challenge Words.** Say the words.

whiplash   fishnet   dimness   potluck   jobless
1    2      1    2     1    2    1    2    1    2

---

B.   **Sentences and Stories.** Read each part of the story. Write the story part number under the picture that goes with each story part.

### The Lost Ship

**Part 1**

   The big ship is at the dock. The men go up a ramp
to the deck of the ship. They set a fishnet on the deck.
Then the ship chugs west. The men will fish from the ship.
With luck, they will get bass to sell.

-----

**Part 2**

   When the sun sets, the men pick up the fishnet.
They fill the big box with bass and shut the lid. At dusk,
the wind sends fog past the ship. The ship is hidden in
the fog. The men cannot see the land. The ship is lost.

-----

**Part 3**

   The ship hits a rock in the sand. The rock rips the ship.
The men jump into the water. With luck, they will get to land.
The men see a lamp on a tug. The tug picks up the men.

-----

**C. Spelling.** Write the words and sentence that your teacher says.

1. _____     3. _____

2. _____     4. _____

5. _____

_____

**D. Practice Activity 1.** Draw a line under the sentence that goes with each picture.

1. The ship will chug up
   to the dock.

   This chap works on the ship.

2. Mom will get fish
   at the shop.

   Mom will whip the eggs.

3. Pam shut off the lamp.

   Pam cannot sit on the
   hot sand.

4. The pup licks him
   on the chin.

   The dog jumps into the pond.

5. Jan and Nan will chat
   in the shop.

   Jan will have potluck
   with Nan.

Correct

E.  **Practice Activity 2.** Read each story. Circle the word that best completes each sentence.

**Story 1**

Chug. Chug. Chug. The big ship will chug into the inlet. The ship will dock. The men will go down the ramp into the ship. The men will get fish off the ship. The men will put the fish in a big box. Then they will shut the box.

1.  The ship will _____ into the inlet.              chug      chap      chip

2.  In the inlet, _____ ship will dock.              whip      thin      this

3.  The men will go down the ramp
    into the _____.                                 lamp      fish      ship

4.  The men will put the _____
    in a big box.                                          ship      fish      whip

5.  The men will _____ the box of fish.             this      shut      dock

**Story 2**

Chip is a chipmunk. He is not thin. When it is dusk, Chip gets nuts from the shed. Chip fills his nest with nuts. Chip cannot get nuts when Ben shuts the shed. Is that chipmunk a pest?

1.  Chip is not _____.                              thin      that      shut

2.  At dusk, Chip gets nuts from the
    _____.                                          shed      nut      shut

3.  Chip cannot get nuts _____
    the shed is shut.                                      chip      when      whip

4.  Is _____ chipmunk a pest?                       that      thin      then

5.  Will Ben _____ the shed?                        chip      thin      shut

☐  Correct

# LESSON 26

**A. New Words.** Say each sound. Say each word.

| | | | |
|---|---|---|---|
| 1. | <u>wh</u> e n | <u>ch</u> i n | <u>th</u> e n |
| 2. | <u>th</u> e m | <u>th</u> i n | <u>sh</u> e d |
| 3. | <u>wh</u> i z | <u>sh</u> u t | <u>sh</u> o t |
| 4. | ch u g | ch u m | sh u n |
| 5. | th a t | ch a p | th i s |

Circle the word that goes with each picture.

1.      when     chin     then

2.      them     thin     shed

3.      whiz     shut     shot

4.      chug     chum     shun

5.      that     chap     this

■ **Sight Words.** Say the words.

said    she    was    some    very    from    down    my    put    saw

■ **Challenge Words.** Say the words.

radish    endless    eggshell    shipment    basket
1   2       1   2       1    2      1    2       1    2

B. **Sentences and Stories.** Read each part of the story. Write the story part number under the picture that goes with each story part.

### Eggs

**Part 1**

Tess had ten hens in a shed. Her job was to get the eggs from the nests. Tess had to bend down to get the hidden eggs. She had to fill a basket with eggs. When the basket had eggs, she went to the hut.

_____

**Part 2**

In the hut, I saw Tess pack some eggs into a big box. I saw her pick up an egg and set it into the box. Tess did not chip the thin eggshell. When she shut the lid of the box, Tess said, "I will sell the eggs at the shop."

_____

**Part 3**

Then I saw Tess put the box of eggs into the van. She set the box on a rack in the back of the van. Tess said, "My van is not very fast, but it will chug to the shop with no mishap. The shop will get eggs, and I will get cash."

_____

**C. Spelling.** Write the words and sentence that your teacher says.

1. _____    3. _____

2. _____    4. _____

5. _____

_____

**D. Practice Activity 1.** Draw a line under the sentence that goes with each picture.

1. Meg has a very thin chin.

   That chap has very thin lips.

2. Tom and Tim lock the shed.

   Tom shuts the lid.

3. Lin digs up a thin radish.

   Lin fills the bucket with eggs.

4. That red dish has a chip.

   The fish is on this dish.

5. Jeff picks up the box of rocks.

   Mom picks up the tot.

Correct

E. **Practice Activity 2.** Read each story. Circle the word that best completes each sentence.

**Story 1**

   Lin dug and dug. Lin dug in the mud. It was an endless job. She dug up a thin radish. It was the last radish. The radish will go in the bucket.

1. Lin dug in the _____.          shun          when          mud

2. It was an _____ job.          endless          ship          chop

3. Lin dug up a _____.          shipment          radish          anthem

4. The radish was _____.          thin          chin          shed

5. The radish will go in the _____.          ship          bucket          shot

**Story 2**

   Jeff has a task. He bends down to get rocks. He puts them in a box. Jeff picks up the big box of rocks. He sets the box in the shed. He shuts the shed. Then Jeff locks the shed.

1. Jeff has a _____.          task          shop          mask

2. Jeff bends down to get _____.          locks          rocks          socks

3. Jeff puts the rocks in a _____.          shut          ship          box

4. Jeff _____ up the big box.          picks          hut          sets

5. Jeff _____ the shed.          rocks          locks          socks

Correct

# LESSON 27

■ **New Sounds.** Say the words.

<u>cl</u>am    <u>br</u>an    <u>cr</u>op    <u>dr</u>ip    <u>fl</u>ed    <u>Fr</u>ed    <u>sl</u>ed    <u>sn</u>ap    <u>sp</u>ed    <u>tw</u>ig

**A.  New Words.** Say each sound. Say each word.

1.   <u>sl</u>  e  d         <u>fl</u>  e  d         <u>br</u>  a  n

2.   <u>Fr</u>  e  d         <u>cr</u>  i  b         <u>sp</u>  e  d

3.   <u>br</u>  i  m         <u>cl</u>  a  m         <u>fl</u>  a  t

4.   sn  a  p         sn  i  p         tw  i  g

5.   cl  a  p         cr  o  p         dr  o  p

Circle the word that goes with each picture.

1.      sled        fled        bran

2.      Fred        crib        sped

3.      brim        clam        flat

4.      snap        snip        twig

5.      clap        crop        drop

108

■ **Sight Words.** Say the words.

snow    said    down    play    put    they    from    she    into    of

■ **Challenge Words.** Say the words.

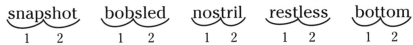

snapshot    bobsled    nostril    restless    bottom
1    2        1    2      1    2      1    2      1    2

B.  **Sentences and Stories.** Read each part of the story. Write the story part number under the picture that goes with each story part.

### The Bobsled Contest

**Part 1**

  The bobsled contest was on the summit of Big Top.x
A path was dug in the snow. The path was not flat.
It had bumps. The path went down the hill.

—————

**Part 2**

  Nick and Jan went to the contest. They had a
red bobsled. They went to the shed at the top of
the path. Nick and Jan put wax on the bottom of
the bobsled. The bobsled must go down the path fast.
It must have no mishaps.

—————

**Part 3**

  Nick and Jan went to the top of the path. The man at
the top said, "Best of luck." Then Nick and Jan ran and
got on the back of the sled. The bobsled sped down
the hill. It hit a rock in the path. Nick and Jan fell off
the sled. They did not panic. They got up and led the
sled off the path. They lost the contest, but they had fun.

—————

**C. Spelling.** Write the words and sentence that your teacher says.

1. _____ 3. _____

2. _____ 4. _____

5. _____

_____

**D. Practice Activity 1.** Draw a line under the sentence that goes with each picture.

1. The bobsled sped down the hill.    The bobsled hit a flat rock.

2. Tess and Bess will clap.    Tess led Bess down the path.

3. Fred will snip the twigs.    Fred will pick up the twigs.

4. The van went down the hill.    The van went to pick up the shipment.

5. Jim will have a nap.    Tim will have a bran muffin.

Correct

**E.  Practice Activity 2.** Read each story. Circle the word that best completes each sentence.

**Story 1**

Kit went to bed. She put her doll in a crib. She did not nap. She did not rest. She got up and went to Mom. Kit said, "Can I get up and have water? I will not drop it."

Mom said, "Yes, you can get up. We will have some bran muffins."

| | | | |
|---|---|---|---|
| 1.  Kit went to _____. | school | fled | bed |
| 2.  Kit put her doll in a _____. | endless | sled | crib |
| 3.  Kit did not _____. | twin | nap | drop |
| 4.  Kit did not _____ the water. | drop | flat | nest |
| 5.  Kit and Mom had _____ muffins. | bran | snapshots | clam |

**Story 2**

Fred was on a sled in the snow. The sled sped down the hill. Fred shot down the hill. Fred won the contest! Brad has a snapshot of Fred on the sled.

| | | | |
|---|---|---|---|
| 1.  Fred was on a _____. | sled | shed | shot |
| 2.  The sled _____ down the hill. | led | sped | drop |
| 3.  Fred _____ down the hill. | brim | sled | shot |
| 4.  Fred won the _____. | contest | bottom | radish |
| 5.  Brad has a _____. | snapshot | restless | shipment |

Correct

# LESSON 28

■ **New Sounds.** Say the words.

<u>st</u>op          <u>pl</u>an    <u>sk</u>in    <u>tr</u>ip

**A. New Words.** Say each sound. Say each word.

| | | | | | |
|---|---|---|---|---|---|
| 1. <u>pl</u> o t | <u>sk</u> i n | <u>st</u> e p |
| 2. <u>fl</u> a p | <u>sk</u> i d | <u>tr</u> i m |
| 3. <u>st</u> o p | <u>sk</u> i p | <u>cr</u> a b |
| 4. fl a g | dr a g | st e m |
| 5. pl a n | St a n | tr i p |

Circle the word that goes with each picture.

1.     plot       skin       step

2.     flap       skid       trim

3.     stop       skip       crab

4.     flag       drag       stem

5.     plan       Stan       trip

■ **Sight Words.** Say the words.
put    said    be    her    children    my    snow    school    of    some

■ **Challenge Words.** Say the words.
traffic    jacket    flapjack    planet    wagon
1  2      1  2      1  2       1  2      1  2

**B.  Sentences and Stories.** Read each part of the story. Write the story part number under the picture that goes with each story part.

### Go West

### Part 1

Peg sat with her husband Stan, Stan said, "I am restless. I wish to go to the West. We cannot get land unless we go. When we get to the West, we can pick a plot of land. Then we can put up a cabin and put in crops."

Peg said, "We do not have kin in the West. It is a risk, but it will be best to go."

_____

### Part 2

Stan and Peg got six ox and a big wagon. Stan said, "We cannot pack much in the wagon." In a box, they put a rug, cups, pans, pots, and a bucket. They put some fabric and denim jackets in the box. In the back of the wagon, they put a big jug of water. They had to sell the rest.

_____

### Part 3

At last, Stan, Peg, and the children went on the trip. Peg sat with the children in the back of the wagon. The little tot sat on her lap. Stan led the six oxen. They went past the cabins to the path. When they got to the path, they did not look back.

_____

113

**C. Spelling.** Write the words and sentence that your teacher says.

1. _____    3. _____

2. _____    4. _____

5. _____

_____

**D. Practice Activity 1.** Fill in each blank with the best word.

| | | | |
|---|---|---|---|
| 1. The children wish to go on a _____. | stem | trip | traffic |
| 2. Jeff dug in the sand to get a _____. | flag | stem | crab |
| 3. His _____ was red from the sun. | skid | step | skin |
| 4. Fred will _____ the sled up the hill. | bran | clam | drag |
| 5. A _____ was on top of the school. | flap | flag | fled |
| 6. The van will _____ in the snow. | skid | skin | stem |
| 7. We will _____ in traffic. | stem | plot | stop |
| 8. Nan shut the _____ of her backpack. | fun | flap | flag |
| 9. Tim and Pam _____ a trip. | plan | skin | drag |
| 10. The children will _____ down the path. | stem | trim | skip |

114

☐ Correct

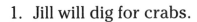

**E.** **Practice Activity 2.** Draw a line under the sentence that goes with each picture.

1. Jill will dig for crabs.        Jill will water the crops.

2. The van went into the traffic.        The ox drags the big box in the sun.

3. Jeff got some mud on his skin.        Jeff got some mud on the rug.

4. Tom steps on the bug.        Tom steps on the mat.

5. Pat had a dish of clams.        The kitten sat on her lap.

6. Bill looks at the flags.        Bill looks at the planets.

7. The red cab sped into traffic.        Kit drops her red jacket.

8. Lin will snip off the stems.        Lin will plan her trip.

Correct          Checking Up          115

# LESSON 29

■ **New Sounds.** Say the words.

Gl<u>en</u>     <u>gr</u>in

**A.  New Words.** Say each sound. Say each word.

1.  <u>gr</u> a b        <u>pl</u> u m        <u>gr</u> i n

2.  <u>fl</u> a t        <u>gr</u> i p        <u>dr</u> u m

3.  <u>cl</u> u b        <u>Gl</u> e n        <u>sl</u> i d

4.  tw i n        gl a d        sp o t

5.  sk i t        dr a g        sp i n

Circle the word that goes with each picture.

1.          grab        plum        grin

2.          flat        grip        drum

3.          club        Glen        slid

4.          twin        glad        spot

5.          skit        drag        spin

■ **Sight Words.** Say the words.

put    said    play    down    children    they    from    she    he    school

■ **Challenge Words.** Say the words.

clinic    unpack    frantic    backdrop    gladness
1  2      1   2      1   2       1    2      1    2

**B.** **Sentences and Stories.** Read each part of the story. Write the story part number under the picture that goes with each story part.

### The Trip

**Part 1**

From sunup to sunset, Stan led the ox down the path. The path was not flat. The wagon had to go up and down hills. The wagon did not stop until sunset. When it did stop, the children were glad to step off the wagon.

_____

**Part 2**

The children did not play. They had to unpack the wagon. They had to drag the tent to a flat spot of land and put it up. Then they set up the cots in the tent. Stan went to a pond to fish. When he had a lot of fish, he went back to the tent. Peg put the fish in a pan. She lit a lamp and set it on a rock. Then the children sat down.

_____

**Part 3**

At last, they got up and went to the tent. Peg shut the flap to stop the wind. She said, "Children, hush. We must be back on the path at sunup. We must get a lot of rest." Then Peg shut off the lamp and went to bed.

_____

**C. Spelling.** Write the words and sentence that your teacher says.

1. _____    3. _____

2. _____    4. _____

5. _____

_____

**D. Practice Activity 1.** Fill in each blank with the best word.

| | | | |
|---|---|---|---|
| spin | skit | flat | twig |
| drum | trip | slid | plum |

1. Did you snap the _____?

2. The top of the shed was _____.

3. Pat has a fat _____ in her dish.

4. Tom can _____ a top.

5. Jeff is in a _____ at school.

6. The sled _____ down the hill.

7. Lin hit the _____.

8. Dad and the twins will go on a _____.

Correct

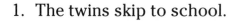

**E.** **Practice Activity 2.** Draw a line under the sentence that goes with each picture.

1. The twins skip to school.          The twins had drums.

2. Tom can get the top to spin.          Tom can grab the bag.

3. Nat and Pat are in the skit.          Nat and Pat are in a club.

4. Bob went to the clinic.          The lad sat on a flat rock.

5. The flag flaps in the wind.          Nick grins with gladness.

6. Nan was glad to win the contest.          Nan had a bucket of fat plums.

7. The van slid in the snow.          She will unpack the eggs.

8. The frantic pup fled.          The cab sped into traffic.

# LESSON 30

**A. New Words.** Say each sound. Say each word.

1. <u>br</u> a n      <u>gr</u> i n      <u>sp</u> o t

2. <u>sn</u> i p      <u>tr</u> a p      <u>sl</u> i m

3. <u>dr</u> i p      <u>gr</u> i p      <u>sl</u> i p

4. cr o p      cl a m      fl i p

5. fr o g      sk i n      st o p

Circle the word that goes with each picture.

1.       bran      grin      spot

2.       snip      trap      slim

3.       drip      grip      slip

4.       crop      clam      flip

5.       frog      skin      stop

■ **Sight Words.** Say the words.

put   was   they   went   into   down   very   we   go   water

■ **Challenge Words.** Say the words.

druggist   rocket   classic   drastic   ballad
1    2       1   2      1   2      1   2      1   2

**B.   Sentences and Stories.** Read each part of the story. Write the story part number under the picture that goes with each story part.

**The Land**

**Part 1**

   At last, Peg, Stan, and the children got to the West. It was the end of the trip. They had big grins. The land was very vast. They got to pick a plot of land. They got to pick the best spot.

_____

**Part 2**

   Stan put up a log cabin. Peg put a rug and cots in the cabin. The children put the pots and pans in a box. Then the children put the denim jackets on the bed. Peg lit a gas lamp. They sat down to rest. They had eggnog and bran muffins.

_____

**Part 3**

   When it was hot, Stan and Peg put in crops. Then they put up a shed for hens. The children will pick the eggs from the nests.

_____

**C. Spelling.** Write the words and sentence that your teacher says.

1. _____    3. _____

2. _____    4. _____

5. _____

   _____

**D. Practice Activity 1.** Fill in each blank with the best word.

1. I saw Tom pick up the _____.          grin     twig     slim

2. Jeff got a _____ on his jacket.        slip     spot     flip

3. We saw Jan _____ in the mud.          club     grip     slip

4. Ten children go on a _____.           trip     trap     twig

5. Lin is very _____.                    slip     sled     slim

6. Water will _____ into the bucket.     drip     trap     clam

7. Pam is _____ to win.                  grin     glad     grip

8. Her _____ will look red from the sun. skin     grin     skip

☐ Correct

**E. Practice Activity 2.** Draw a line under the sentence that goes with each picture.

1. Don and Jan went on a trip.

    The rocket will land on that spot.

2. The water will drip into the tent.

    We set a trap in the cabin.

3. Nan must grip the clam bucket.

    The lad licks the snow off his lips.

4. Rick will grip the twig.

    The slim pig had a big grin.

5. Tess sells bran muffins.

    The druggist stops in traffic.

6. The twins sit on the sled.

    The twins will slip in the snow.

7. Lin set the wig in the box.

    Lin is glad to win.

8. Stan and Peg put up a log cabin.

    Peg mends the rip.

☐ Correct

# Word Lists

| LESSON 1 | LESSON 2 | LESSON 3 | LESSON 4 | LESSON 5 | LESSON 6 |
|----------|----------|----------|----------|----------|----------|
| **New Words** | **New Words** | **New Words** | **New Words** | **New Words** | **New Words** |
| am | fix | bat | bib | on | Bob |
| in | ad | cat | Jim | ox | job |
| Sam | wax | his | bad | mob | lot |
| an | win | him | ham | mop | jot |
| Nan | van | can | did | map | him |
| fit | sap | bit | Dad | rat | box |
| man | sip | had | pad | rot | cab |
| sat | mad | hid | hat | fox | cob |
| sit | lid | pat | big | rod | hot |
| fat | map | pit | dip | rid | tip |
| sad | fin | hit | hit | not | hit |
| lip | fan | tan | mat | Nat | top |
| rip | rat | tin | gas | Bob | dot |
| ran | six | tap | has | rib | hip |
| lap | mix | tip | his | nod | hop |
| **Sight Words** | **Sight Words** | **Sight Words** | **Sight Words** | **Sight Words** | **Sight Words** |
| people | water | have | with | after | some |
| school | you | her | no | of | of |
| to | are | and | go | from | with |
| little | my | we | she | to | after |
| on | was | he | my | with | from |
| was | people | little | to | people | was |
| he | school | water | water | water | school |
| see | little | people | on | he | to |
| a | to | see | little | school | go |
| the | on | to | was | my | she |
| **Challenge Words** | **Challenge Words** | **Challenge Words** | **Challenge Words** | **Challenge Words** | **Challenge Words** |
| admit | tidbit | cabin | napkin | cannot | robin |
| fabric | limit | catnip | picnic | fossil | avid |
| rabbit | satin | hatpin | timid | hatbox | bobbin |
| rapid | valid | atlas | zigzag | madcap | canvas |
| attic | axis | panic | candid | mishap | catnap |

| LESSON 7 | LESSON 8 | LESSON 9 | LESSON 10 | LESSON 11 | LESSON 12 |
|---|---|---|---|---|---|
| **New Words** | **New Words** | **New Words** | **New Words** | **New Words** | **New Words** |
| cot | up | bud | hug | Ed | get |
| cat | us | bid | big | fed | pet |
| tot | run | but | bug | set | hem |
| fox | rub | cub | pup | sit | bed |
| jog | sod | cab | tug | men | hum |
| jig | mug | tub | tag | red | pen |
| got | fun | cup | hum | not | pan |
| sop | fan | cod | cut | led | leg |
| cod | sun | hut | ham | lad | log |
| cap | pin | not | rut | web | lug |
| not | mud | nut | bun | met | bet |
| log | mad | hot | sub | lot | bat |
| pat | pun | bus | sob | let | ten |
| pot | rug | dug | jug | get | jet |
| pit | rig | dog | rot | rod | jot |
| **Sight Words** | **Sight Words** | **Sight Words** | **Sight Words** | **Sight Words** | **Sight Words** |
| put | they | saw | into | look | where |
| from | very | went | I | down | children |
| after | have | very | very | some | some |
| with | from | they | saw | saw | see |
| to | little | of | some | very | very |
| people | water | she | they | they | my |
| on | he | are | go | after | with |
| my | people | have | from | was | on |
| water | and | from | after | little | water |
| little | on | her | with | from | I |
| **Challenge Words** | **Challenge Words** | **Challenge Words** | **Challenge Words** | **Challenge Words** | **Challenge Words** |
| tactic | until | public | habit | upset | hectic |
| mimic | sunup | ribbon | submit | exit | helmet |
| comma | muffin | campus | summit | septic | hidden |
| tonsil | rustic | hiccup | vivid | sadden | denim |
| cosmic | suntan | cotton | comic | panel | puppet |

| LESSON 13 | LESSON 14 | LESSON 15 | LESSON 16 | LESSON 17 | LESSON 18 |
|---|---|---|---|---|---|
| **New Words** | **New Words** | **New Words** | **New Words** | **New Words** | **New Words** |
| beg | off | Bill | lass | math | path |
| yet | miss | huff | hill | neck | back |
| pat | mitt | dill | less | Nick | hush |
| yes | hill | doll | gill | pack | wish |
| Don | mass | less | loss | path | with |
| den | pass | loss | Jess | cash | tack |
| wed | less | fuss | Bess | peck | bath |
| pet | jazz | mess | off | bath | mash |
| pot | kiss | hiss | moss | fish | kick |
| pit | puff | Jill | miss | rock | tuck |
| pep | putt | mutt | toss | dish | cash |
| Mom | Jeff | boss | doll | moth | rush |
| hen | egg | fill | fill | dash | rash |
| him | will | Bess | Jeff | Jack | lock |
| leg | fill | fell | boss | rack | luck |
| **Sight Words** | **Sight Words** | **Sight Words** | **Sight Words** | **Sight Words** | **Sight Words** |
| work | be | tree | went | down | children |
| said | play | snow | said | went | into |
| where | saw | with | with | play | went |
| saw | after | children | play | where | play |
| very | with | after | snow | water | some |
| school | children | see | after | some | school |
| her | some | they | school | saw | of |
| have | to | very | put | from | with |
| to | my | be | on | put | he |
| he | from | she | have | after | to |
| **Challenge Words** | **Challenge Words** | **Challenge Words** | **Challenge Words** | **Challenge Words** | **Challenge Words** |
| rotten | sunset | sunlit | tomcat | dishrag | backlog |
| comet | kitten | tennis | bellhop | bathtub | backpack |
| fatten | eggnog | suffix | bonnet | within | packet |
| inlet | signal | sadness | offset | vanish | punish |
| goblet | velvet | unless | hilltop | racket | ticket |

| LESSON 19 | LESSON 20 | LESSON 21 | LESSON 22 | LESSON 23 | LESSON 24 |
|---|---|---|---|---|---|
| **New Words** | **New Words** | **New Words** | **New Words** | **New Words** | **New Words** |
| duck | rust | nest | jump | risk | when |
| dock | fast | lamp | pump | test | ship |
| bath | bump | must | band | west | chip |
| path | lend | last | hand | desk | chat |
| deck | lent | bump | tent | land | that |
| sack | mask | fist | ramp | best | shed |
| mash | list | sent | mend | bent | this |
| sock | rest | cast | dust | damp | thus |
| mesh | lump | send | dusk | ramp | chop |
| sash | lost | desk | vast | bump | whip |
| tack | mend | went | tusk | fast | shop |
| mush | lamp | fund | task | pest | then |
| lick | hand | sand | wind | past | whiz |
| pick | hint | mask | pond | lump | chin |
| gush | ask | mint | husk | pond | thud |
| **Sight Words** | **Sight Words** | **Sight Words** | **Sight Words** | **Sight Words** | **Sight Words** |
| down | down | for | work | work | work |
| went | went | she | down | she | down |
| play | work | down | she | down | children |
| she | put | very | play | where | tree |
| water | from | children | from | children | said |
| saw | very | they | see | they | into |
| into | into | into | into | have | he |
| with | of | look | look | into | to |
| after | be | have | of | be | from |
| to | was | see | he | look | saw |
| **Challenge Words** | **Challenge Words** | **Challenge Words** | **Challenge Words** | **Challenge Words** | **Challenge Words** |
| backup | insist | disgust | dentist | adjust | chipmunk |
| polish | absent | contest | intend | extend | nutshell |
| publish | picket | discuss | invent | husband | shamrock |
| bucket | backrest | pocket | sandbox | indent | anthem |
| hammock | invest | jackpot | locket | socket | banish |

| LESSON 25 | LESSON 26 | LESSON 27 | LESSON 28 | LESSON 29 | LESSON 30 |
|---|---|---|---|---|---|
| **New Words** | **New Words** | **New Words** | **New Words** | **New Words** | **New Words** |
| shed | when | sled | plot | grab | bran |
| this | chin | fled | skin | plum | grin |
| shop | then | bran | step | grin | spot |
| that | them | Fred | flap | flat | snip |
| thin | thin | crib | skid | grip | trap |
| chin | shed | sped | trim | drum | slim |
| ship | whiz | brim | stop | club | drip |
| chap | shut | clam | skip | Glen | grip |
| chat | shot | flat | crab | slid | slip |
| whip | chug | snap | flag | twin | crop |
| chug | chum | snip | drag | glad | clam |
| chip | shun | twig | stem | spot | flip |
| then | that | clap | plan | skit | frog |
| shut | chap | crop | Stan | drag | skin |
| when | this | drop | trip | spin | stop |
| **Sight Words** | **Sight Words** | **Sight Words** | **Sight Words** | **Sight Words** | **Sight Words** |
| go | said | snow | put | put | put |
| down | she | said | said | said | was |
| to | was | down | be | play | they |
| work | some | play | her | down | went |
| they | very | put | children | children | into |
| some | from | they | my | they | down |
| from | down | from | snow | from | very |
| into | my | she | school | she | we |
| see | put | into | of | he | go |
| water | saw | of | some | school | water |
| **Challenge Words** | **Challenge Words** | **Challenge Words** | **Challenge Words** | **Challenge Words** | **Challenge Words** |
| whiplash | radish | snapshot | traffic | clinic | druggist |
| fishnet | endless | bobsled | jacket | unpack | rocket |
| dimness | eggshell | nostril | flapjack | frantic | classic |
| potluck | shipment | restless | planet | backdrop | drastic |
| jobless | basket | bottom | wagon | gladness | ballad |